Presented to

Summer Shannon

for excellence in the
Redwood Empire Mathematics
Tournament

Director

RECREATIONS IN LOGIC

D.G. WELLS

DOVER PUBLICATIONS, INC.
NEW YORK

Published in Canada by General Publishing Com-
pany, Ltd., 30 Lesmill Road, Don Mills, Toronto,
Ontario.
Published in the United Kingdom by Constable
and Company, Ltd., 10 Orange Street, London
WC2H 7EG.

Recreations in Logic is a new work, first published
by Dover Publications, Inc., in 1979.

International Standard Book Number: 0-486-23895-4
Library of Congress Catalog Card Number: 79-51882

Manufactured in the United States of America
Dover Publications, Inc.
180 Varick Street
New York, N.Y. 10014

CONTENTS

PUZZLES

1. Chris's Kisses

Rearrange these words to form an intelligible sentence, inserting punctuation and capitalizing words as necessary.

no but now more so chris chris chris kris criss chriss cross cross cross crosss crossed crossed crossing krised kissed kisses caress

2. Missing Quickie

C   LOOPSEEND

Not a Dutch name, but a sign. Where would you expect to see it, and what is missing?

3. Bridgit's Bar

David and Graham were playing pool. "Who's winning?" asked Bridgit from behind the bar. "Nothing in it," replied David, "though it's a high scoring game—we've scored nearly 250 points between us."

"What is more," added Graham, "the total exactly equals the product of the differences between our ages. All three of us, that is."

"That's not very useful information, it's ambiguous," said David.

"All right, let's add that double my age plus your age comes to two less than four times Bridgit's age."

"It's still ambiguous."

"True—but you could reach Bridgit's age whichever possibility you chose."

How old is Bridgit?

4. Behind the Scenes

The results were about to be announced in the annual Ruritanian song festival, but there was apparently some delay. Gradually the word was passed round that one of the four finalists, instead of giving three marks to the other finalist he rated highest, and two marks for the next best finalist and one mark for the third best (naturally no finalist was asked to rate his own song), had reversed the marks given, hoping to favor his own chances. He had given one mark to his best choice, two marks to his middle choice and three marks to the finalist he actually thought worst.

The commotion was of course tremendous and it only increased when it was revealed that two of the other finalists had taken exactly the same dishonest step in the hope, so they thought, of improving their chances.

Before these revelations were made all four finalists had been tied on six points. When the judges eventually reversed the marking orders of the three dishonest finalists, in what place did the honest singer find himself?

5. Sizzling Sermon

The curate of Lower Purdham was notorious for his fiery sermons, not least with his uncle, who was the local landowner and bigwig and did not appreciate what he took to be frequent references to his wealth and social position. One day his uncle and aunt were visiting him as he was preparing one of his sermons and his aunt, glancing over his shoulder was horrified to see that it started off, in the curate's hand, "UNCLE AND I SHALL OWE DEVIL . . ." Quite apart from the poor standard of English, this was clearly going to be a hellfire sermon of the first order, and she hastened to tell her husband.

In the ensuing explosion a lot of hard words were spoken, but to no purpose, as became apparent when the curate explained how his sermon actually started. How did it start?

6. Giving Change

When Peter went into the shop he had just two coins in his pocket. He made a purchase and left the shop with three coins in his pocket. As he did so he worked out that he could not have spent less and taken out only three coins. He went next door and spent some more money, emerging with four coins, again spending the least amount of money which allowed this to happen. Finally, he made his third purchase, the smallest that allowed him to leave with only five coins. He had spent almost exactly one-third of his money. What coins did he start with? (Note: only United Kingdom coinage is involved, of these denominations: ½, 1, 2, 5, 10 and 50 pence.)

7. Looking Both Ways

Coming into work by bus, I pass the door of what looks like a garage, on which I read this obscure message. Your puzzle is to say what message, if that is the right word, do I read on my return home?

```
E E T I  I Y
S P L D P T
P E S   E P
  L A   T
  L   I E
```

8. Groovy Sequences

Here are three sequences. They are examples of GROOVY sequences. When you have studied them and decided what makes them GROOVY, test your insight by completing the fourth GROOVY sequence which has exactly two numbers missing.

1st:	1	2	2	2	2	3	4	8	9
2nd:	1	2	3	4	5	6	7		
3rd:	1	2	3	3	5	6	7		
4th:	1	1	2	2	—	—			

9. Relative Volumes

Calculation of the volumes of pyramids can be a bit tricky. Not this puzzle, though. What are the relative volumes of a triangular and a square pyramid, all of whose edges are of equal length? If you can multiply by two you can solve this problem—at least that is all the *calculation* you need!

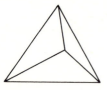 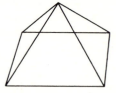

10. Parallelepiped

This shape is an example of a parallelepiped, that is, a shape all of whose six faces are parallelograms. Most regrettably we do not have any parallelograms with which readers might make their own parallelepipeds, but we do have a large number of identical squares. If we give you sixteen of these squares, and a supply of adhesive tape, can you make a parallelepiped? Although a cube is a parallelepiped, a cube is not an acceptable solution!

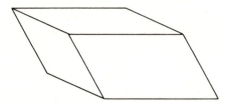

11. Tell Me the Way To Go Home

Tom Farley had been playing darts with friends and he had drunk a bit, so when he set off for home, he felt a little confused. When he reached the Horse and Groom he became even more muddled, because he remembered that there were two routes home from the Horse and Groom, each of equal length. So he stepped inside, had a drink to clear his head, emerged, tossed a coin and turned left towards the Rose. Arriving at the Rose, he recalled that two routes of identical length also existed from the Rose to his house, so he stepped in for another quick pint, left just on closing time, tossed a coin to decide which way to go, and returned home feeling that the evening had been well spent. Just where does Tom Farley live?

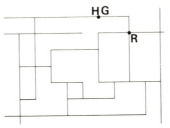

12. Parking Lot

Two straight lines only will divide this parking lot into four parts, each containing one car of each of the seven makes. But beware! The answer is not quite as simple as it seems!

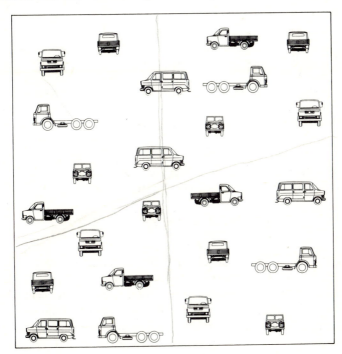

13. Triangular Trisection

To cut an equilateral triangle into three identical shapes is simplicity itself, as these figures show. However, it becomes quite a teaser with this extra condition: none of the cuts can go through the center of the triangle! The center point must be definitely inside one of the thirds. Of course, more than three pieces are required, so that at least one of the identical shapes will be made up from two or more pieces. The question is—What is the smallest number of pieces required in all?

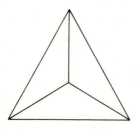 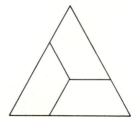

14. The Walrus and the Carpenter

It is a little-known fact, which Lewis Carroll was careful to conceal, that the Walrus and the Carpenter in *Through the Looking Glass* accompanied their meal of oysters with a large quantity of white wine, and became, as a result, rather drunk. This explains of course why two such sober and inoffensive creatures burst into song on a terpsichorean theme. It also explains, if it does not excuse, the rather unkind remark that the Walrus addressed to the Carpenter as the latter swallowed the very last oyster, which remark happens to be an anagram of these words:

HELLO RAVE FIERY HUSSY.

15. Unsymmetrical Symmetry

It was the King of Hexagonia's birthday, and as a foreign guest I had been invited to watch the special maneuvers of his ten-man bodyguard. To the sounds of martial music they formed and reformed their patterns in stately procession, as in my illustrations, but always in such a way that no row in any of three directions ever contained an odd number of men. The pageantry of the occasion and the elegance and symmetry of the patterns they made were delightful. Their last pattern, however, surprised me. It was obviously considered to be the peak of their performance. My host turned and whispered to me, "Such exquisitely unsymmetrical symmetry." It was indeed completely unsymmetrical, though the same condition still obtained. It was impossible to draw any straight line across the figure which would divide it into two halves which were mirror-images of each other. What was this final arrangement?

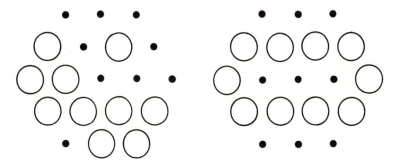

16. A Mon-ster Puzzle

This is a *mon,* a Japanese family crest. Janet wanted to show it in her project on Japanese history and she was just about to cut two equal squares of gummed paper, one black and one white, into quarters and stick them down so that each overlapped a square of the opposite color, when it struck her that eight pieces might not be necessary. Indeed, they were not, and eventually she managed to make the *mon* by using fewer pieces. How many separate pieces did she use?

17. To Separate or Not To Separate

I visited our local carpenter the other day to buy some wood and found him playing with this curious-looking cube. I thought at first that it was made of two pieces that would come apart; then I was not so sure. He wouldn't tell me, or let me handle the cube, but he did hold it firmly while I measured: each side was three inches long and the cuts (I could not tell how deep they were), were through the mid-points of each side and to within three-quarters of an inch of the edges at opposite corners.

Can you say whether the cube could possibly have been made of two pieces which would come apart?

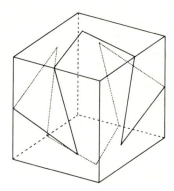

18. April Fool

If you have ever been caught out by an April Fool joke, here is a chance to show how smart you really are. Imagine that these four letters are made of cardboard. How can they be cut into several pieces which will fit together to form a perfect square? Not an easy task!

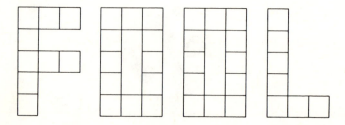

19. Skew Addition

In this sum, the powers of 3 have been written under each other, but with each unit displaced one to the right compared to the preceding number. Assuming the powers of 3 are added up forever in this manner, what will the answer be?

$$1$$
$$3$$
$$9$$
$$27$$
$$81$$
$$243$$
$$729$$
$$2187$$
$$. \; . \; . \; .$$

20. Addled Ladders

Mr. and Mrs. Newly had just moved into their new house and were standing in the kitchen watching the builders who were still putting on the finishing touches, trudging back and forth with their ladders.

In fact, just as they stood there, three men with three identical ladders on their shoulders walked past, two from right to left and one from left to right. The rungs moving past each other were rather a strain on Mr. and Mrs. Newly's eyes, but they could see quite large gaps between the rungs of the three ladders. To be precise: (1) How large a gap could they be certain of seeing between the rungs at any moment in time? (2) How large a gap could they be certain of seeing over a period of time as the ladders moved past?

21. To Spy or Not To Spy

Ravioli al Sugo, the brilliant spy, has had his cover blown by counterintelligence. He has only a short time in which to say goodbye to his beautiful girl friend Granita, collect vital documents from his fellow conspirators Parmess and Cheese and get the first train out of town. Naturally, in this predicament he cannot risk being seen twice in the same place, so starting from R he wishes to visit G, P and C and get to the train T, in that order, without anywhere crossing his path. How would you advise him?

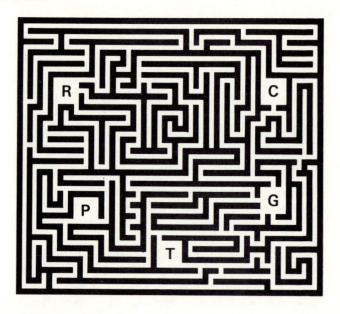

22. A Double Strip

A strip of paper is folded once, as in our figure. At what angle must it be folded so that the area of the strip, which is now of double thickness, is as small as possible?

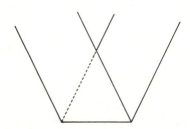

23. Electronic Lullaby

Our small neighbor was given an electronics set for Christmas and we have had no peace since. His latest model is an electronic organ. Unfortunately, it only plays three notes: a high note, *ping*, a middle note *mmmmm*, and a low note, *boing*. He has wired these up so that the same note repeated, for example *ping–ping*, is immediately followed by an *mmmmm*. A note followed by a lower note is followed in turn by *ping*, and a note following a lower note is then followed by a *boing*.

Really quite impressive for a twelve year old, but the contraption is getting on our nerves. Can you explain why?

24. A Giant Difference

You are asked to place the digits one to nine in the cells of this figure so that the sum of all the differences between pairs which are adjacent horizontally or vertically (but *not* diagonally) is as great as possible. There are twelve such differences, two from each row and column. You can find many solutions, but they are all related in a very simple manner.

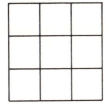

25. An Odd Problem

In this network, ten circles are joined by nineteen lines. What is the smallest number of lines which must be removed to leave a network in which an even number of lines go to every circle?

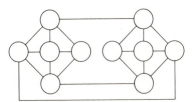

26. Maid To Tease

This is a plan of millionaire ship owner V. Triangulakis's penthouse flat. As you can see, each of the twenty-five rooms has a door to each adjacent room. Unfortunately, this exotic design poses problems to the maid on her daily round, in which she must visit as many rooms as possible but is forbidden to visit any room twice or even go through a door twice. She can start her daily round in any room she chooses. How many rooms is she obliged to miss out each day?

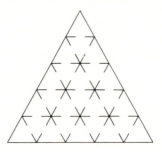

27. Table Cross

Mrs. Dunphy is expecting some visitors and she wants to quickly make a cloth to cover her table, her usual table cloth having been badly damaged. Unfortunately, the only piece of material she possesses which is anything like large enough is this awkward shape.

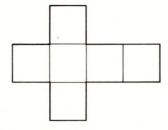

Is Mrs. Dunphy dismayed? Not a bit! She thinks for a moment and then makes three cuts and sews the pieces together. The result is not a square, but it covers her square table very well indeed. What has she done?

28. Double Riddle

This is a riddle with two answers. The two answers are associated with each other (the association is English rather than American), and each line refers to both. So, for example, the first letter of each answer is in CABBAGE but not in KINGS.

My first is in cabbage but not in kings,
My second in house but not in wings.
My third in rex, maybe in regina,
My fourth is most singular, no letter's finer.
My fifth and my sixth in good standing a pair,
My next two in damage—look for them there.
In days and in years you'll discover my last,
My whole is approaching as soon as it's past.

29. Brass or Rubber

This figure shows five rings, four of brass and one of rubber, lying almost flat on a table. Naturally the rubber ring is quite flexible, while the brass rings are flat and rigid. All we ask you to do is to say which of the rings is made of rubber.

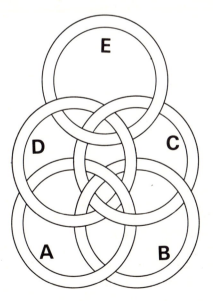

30. Start Counting

Nothing could be simpler than this teaser. If you can count, it's all yours. How many triangles are there in this figure?

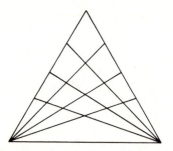

31. Can-Can Strip

This is an ordinary cylindrical tin can, eight inches in height and nine inches in circumference. Beside it is a long strip of paper of uniform width, two inches to be precise. The strip of paper is wound smoothly round the can without overlapping itself, and neatly trimmed where it crosses the top and bottom rims of the can. If as a result the strip covers exactly one-half of the curved surface of the can, what is the length of this cut where it was trimmed?

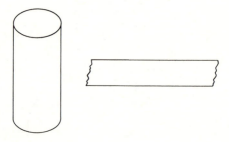

32. Rice Division

Mr. and Mrs. Lo Hun were poor peasant farmers, so when Mrs. Lo Hun accidentally smashed the measuring bowl which she used for measuring out the rice, she was very upset. Fortunately, her husband was skilled in the traditional art of sword fighting, and she brightened up considerably when he took a strong cardboard box of rectangular shape and, with the minimum necessary number of clean plane cuts with his sword, produced a substitute for her bowl which actually measured out one, two, three or four measures of rice, according to her choice.

How many cuts did her husband make, and what shape was the final article?

33. U or Non-U

The number of ways in which this pentomino can be placed on this square is considerable, but the puzzle is not to count them. No, you are asked to say how many of the squares must be removed or blacked out so that no pentomino of this shape can be placed on the area remaining. Of course, the object is to remove the minimum number of squares which will achieve this end.

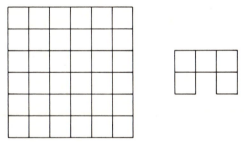

34. World Without End

In this 5 x 5 square, you are asked to imagine that the top edge and the bottom edge are next to each other, as if the square were wrapped round a cylinder. So if you leave the first square at the top edge, as the solid line shows, you will immediately reappear at the bottom edge, moving into the second square.

Similarly, the right and left-hand edges are next to each other. So leaving the right-hand edge along the dashed arrow, you immediately enter the third square of the left-hand side, traveling in the same direction.

The puzzle is this: How can five pieces be placed, one in each of five cells of the square, so that you can visit them all by moving in one straight line (moving off an edge and back onto the opposite edge when necessary); or, alternately, you can visit them all by moving in another straight line in a different direction?

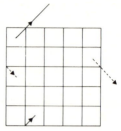

35. Trigger Happy

"So how much do we know?" asked Patterson, doodling with his pencil on the desk.

"It's a five-figure number and it's a perfect square," replied Gerson, "but don't forget that if we get the wrong number the mechanism will jam and we'll lose all chance of detonating it." He drummed his fingers. The phone rang. He picked it up.

"Good heavens! Yes!" He looked at Patterson. "The first two figures are 69, and it reads the same either way! That must fix it, surely? The number is palindromic." Patterson scribbled quickly on his pad. "26 . . . 265 . . . 264, ah, 264 squared is 69696, just a moment . . . mmmm, that's it." He looked up at Gerson and grinned. Gerson picked up the phone and spoke quickly, then sat back and said nothing. After several minutes, the phone rang again and he picked it up confidently. "Yes? It's . . . jammed?" Beads of sweat appeared on his forehead and Patterson felt sick. What had gone wrong?

36. The Language of Animals

In this passage are concealed the names of a number of creatures; for example, in the second and third words taken together you will find BEAR. What are the other hidden creatures?

"The club, earlier attractive, was plain and drab. Bits of paper, peeling and fading on the walls, naked bulbs and a scowling servant who shared the now-littered carpet with beer cans and a stench of cigarette butts—was this her one landfall, her sole refuge?"

37. Dudley No More

Mr. Door and Mrs. Door, many years ago, had a daughter called Petula, or Pet for short. Mr. Door was a keen puzzler and he made a little sum such that every different letter in it stood for a different digit from one to nine, and the sum of course was correct when turned into numbers. It was:

$$PA + MA = PET.$$

Many years passed and Pet married a young man called Patrick, Pat for short, and they produced an offspring called Dudley. Mr. Door made up another sum to go with the first, using the same letters for the same digits:

$$PET + PAT = DUD.$$

Unfortunately, Dudley died at a young age by falling into the washing machine, which rinsed him too thoroughly, so there was no fourth generation and no more sums. What were the two sums?

38. A Boiling Problem

For heating, three students sharing a flat use a one-bar electric fire which runs off its own meter. They have a very simple system for paying for the electricity they use—whenever the meter runs out, whoever is using the fire at the time puts in a fivepenny piece. To their distress however, they have recently kept a record of the money each of them has put in and have discovered that it is not proportional to the time for which each has been using the fire.

What is wrong, and what would you advise them to do?

39. The Chipped Bowl

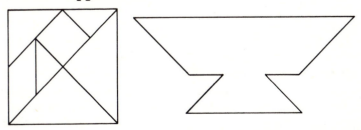

With the seven Tangram pieces it is possible to make this bowl.

Curiously enough, it is also possible to make this bowl with a chip out of it (again using all seven pieces). All you are asked to do is to show how both bowls are fitted together.

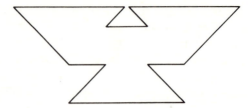

40. A Bed of Roses

Mr. Clattie is a keen gardener and quite mathematical. The other day he was in the local pub describing his latest exercise in geometrical gardening, or harmonious horticulture, as he likes to call it. "I've divided the lawn by a grid of one-yard squares," he said, "and put six stakes into six of the corners of these squares. I put a piece of string round the stakes, cut out the turf inside the string, and planted roses. Neat, don't you think? Sort of random, but clean-cut."

"Very nice, Bill," said the landlord, "but why don't you just tell us how big your bed of roses is, and we'll drink to a lot of bloomin' flowers next summer."

"Well, if I tell you that there were seven of the corner points of the squares inside the string outline and none actually immediately under the string, that's enough, isn't it?"

"Bill Clattie," said the landlord, "if you're not careful you could make yourself quite unpopular. But I'll drink to you anyway. Cheers!"

What was the area of Mr. Clattie's flowerbed?

41. Not Quite Useless

The well-known firm of Shyster, Shyster, Shyster and Sons is in trouble. The calculating machines they use to work out their giant fees have broken down. One will only add, another will only subtract, the third will only multiply, and the last will only divide. Which machine will be of most use to the poor clerks, who are totally brainless when it comes to doing mental arithmetic?

42. An Intimate Affair

At an intimate little soirée given by Lady What's-her-name the other evening, each man danced with exactly three women and each woman with exactly three men. What is more, each pair of men had exactly two dancing partners in common. An admirable arrangement which pleased Lady What's-her-name no end and also gives the reader enough information to discover exactly how intimate that soirée was. How many people attended?

43. A Cushy Number

Professor Canon was playing billiards as usual when I arrived, and as usual he was playing on a table of his own design, in the form of an equilateral triangle with perfect cushions.

"What are you practicing?" I asked, as he polished the groove in his chin with the cue. "Playing the ball parallel to the cushes," he replied, "same direction, same force, every time. That's why I'm using a stop-watch, as you can see." I didn't see, but I watched him play a few shots and soon realized how easily he could check the direction and the strength of his shots. Do you?

44. The Golden Handshake

Jeff Snatchem and his gang of ruffians were about to share the loot from their latest outrage. Unfortunately, when each man had been given an equal share, some loot was left over, enough to give all but a handful of the men an extra gold piece. The argument over this remainder was just becoming violent when some more gang members arrived, and all the loot was shared out again to include them. Each man received the same as before and there were now twenty fewer gold pieces left over. Before another argument could start, the last members of the gang arrived, and there was a third share-out. Each man received the same as before, but there were ten fewer pieces left over. The handful of men who arrived late were sent to the local tavern to spend the remainder on food and drink, one-half of the men drinking beer and one-third drinking smuggled French brandy. While they celebrate, can you work out each man's share and how many members there are in the gang altogether?

45. Artful Arithmetic

Johnny is not very keen on mathematics, so he jumped at what seemed to be a quick way of discovering which of two fractions is the larger. Asked to find, for example, the larger of $\frac{2}{5}$ and $\frac{3}{7}$, he altered each fraction by replacing its denominator with the difference between the original denominator and the numerator. Thus $\frac{2}{5}$ he altered to $2/(5-2)$ or $\frac{2}{3}$.

So his original pair became $\frac{2}{3}$ and $\frac{3}{4}$, and he immediately changed these again in exactly the same way into $\frac{2}{1}$ and $\frac{3}{1}$, concluding triumphantly that the second fraction, originally $\frac{3}{7}$, is the larger of the two.

The teacher's problem, and of course yours, is to decide whether Johnny's method is valid, or whether it is nonsense and his correct conclusion in this example is merely a lucky fluke.

46. A Non-Slippery Problem

The figure shows four rollers which roll against each other, in sequence, without slipping. The diameters of A and D are four inches and six inches respectively. B is twice the diameter of C and the total diameters of B and C together are equal to four times the diameter of A. If A is rotating at three revolutions per second, how fast will D rotate?

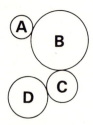

47. Coming and Going

"It's a funny journey when I visit you," said Mrs. Woolidge to her daughter. "I get the train and change at the junction. I arrive at platform three and I have to walk over to platform five. That's all right, but when I'm going home in the opposite direction I also arrive at platform three and walk over to platform five, and each time I arrive facing in the same direction."

"Well, of course you do," said her daughter, "you can't have trains going in opposite directions on the same track, now, can you?"

"I don't like it," insisted Mrs. Woolidge. "I think that next time I'll come by bus."

Of course the explanation is really very simple. Can you draw the lines in and out of the juction?

48. Word Squares Made Easy

What is the largest number of different letters that can appear in a 4 x 4 word square? Of course, er, that number is not necessary. If you had been on holiday in Morocco last summer, you might just possibly have found yourself sitting under a sandarac tree, otherwise known as the arar, thinking of your mother. The temptation to jot down our first word square on your cuff would have been irresistible. Just as you are doing so a man strolls by in a striped abba, a Syrian garment of goat's or camel's hair. You wonder momentarily why an abba should be worn in Morocco, but soon you are concentrating on the potential of the word itself. Realizing that it was a mistake to use indelible ink on your cuff, you jot down our second word square on the back of your hand.

You are now absolutely wide awake, and seeing an elderly gentleman driving down the main street in an ancient jalopy blowing his horn at nothing in particular, you are immediately reminded of your own uncle, whose name also means a very fragrant essential oil, and you jot down our third word square, to be found only in Solutions. Only two letters. There is a lot to be said for the simple life.

M	A	M	A
A	R	A	R
M	A	M	A
A	R	A	R

A	B	B	A
B	O	O	B
B	O	O	B
A	B	B	A

49. Advanced Word Maths

You may recall from your schooldays that any square grid can be turned into a larger square grid by adding a border. For example, to turn a 3 x 3 square into a 4 x 4 square, you can add a row of squares along the top and down the right-hand side, plus one in the corner, leading to the number pattern: $3^2 + 3 + 3 + 1 = 4^2$.

The same can be done for word squares. For example, if you square a meadow and add an appropriate three letter word along two sides and a royal letter in the corner, you will immediately have grasped the solution to this problem. If the answer still escapes you, it may help you to know that any two adjacent borders removed from the final square will leave a three-by-three word square. Two edges in particular should be looked at carefully—if you let the drink slip away, everything will be over.

50. Speedy Gonzales

The other day, traveling by London underground, I dashed onto the platform just as my train was moving out. I caught the next one, and left the exit of my destination station at exactly the same time as I would have done had I not missed the first train. Both trains traveled at the same speed, no acts of God were involved, and I didn't have to rush to make up for the lost time. Explanation please?

51. Youth and Age

"Wow! Macroscopic baby!" cried Patsy, "that's the most visible thing. . . ."

"Patsy!" said Alice severely, "Cool it! Oops, what am I saying?"

"You meant to say, 'Control yourself,'" put in Grandfather kindly, "the semantic vacuity of Patsy's speech is infectious. I sometimes wonder how he'll speak when he is my age."

"You're an old square," said Patsy rudely, "and when I am half your present age you will still be a square, and you were a square when I was born."

"But when you are half my present age, you will be a square twice over," replied Grandfather, smiling, "and in the meantime you will be a square twice." He blew a smoke ring past Patsy's left ear. Patsy looked gloomy. What are the ages of Patsy and Grandfather?

52. Round the Bends

We had a terrible time moving. Everything had to go along this narrow corridor with an angle in it. Each shelf of the bookcase we slid round with one long edge on the floor and the other long edge vertically above it. The bed was a nightmare, but the piano was worst of all because it was too heavy to lift and it's five feet long. We pushed it round half an inch at a time and it still got scratched. I worked out later that we couldn't have got anything bigger round that corner—bigger in horizontal cross section, I mean. It could have been longer and thinner, or shorter and fatter, but not bigger in area. Here's a sketch of the piano going round. Both parts of the corridor are the same width. Now you can work out the length of the bookshelves, can't you?

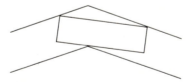

53. Beet This

An intelligent beetle called Bert (why should flies have all the fun?) was walking over the surface of a cube. "Um, three edges and three faces meeting at each vertex," he mumbled to himself. Instantly there was a great flash and the cube blew up and he found himself walking across an infinite plane surface. "Um, four edges and four faces at each vertex, very interesting," he muttered, when Swoosh! the whole plane crinkled up and he found himself inside a vast space, stretching as far as he could see. Fortunately he was too stunned to say anything, though he did notice that five edges and five faces, all square, met at every vertex. What was the simplest shape in which he could have found himself?

54. An Amazing Escape

Archaeologists, more than most scientists, destroy cherished myths with every discovery they make. When they claim, however, that the Labyrinth which trapped Theseus was merely the rooms of a palace with which he was unfamiliar, they are going too far. They fail to appreciate that when you are being hotly pursued by a Minotaur, you MUST take every opportunity to turn left or right to escape the beast, however quickly you might otherwise escape in a straight line. Naturally Theseus, who entered by the south entrance to the palace, wanted to get to his beloved Ariadne, who was waiting just outside the north entrance, as quickly as possible. What was his shortest route if he was to evade the Minotaur?

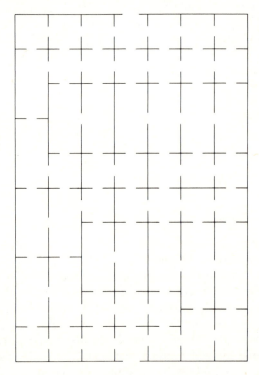

55. Pasternes

"That's not how you spell 'pasterns,'" I said.

"Of course it isn't," he replied, "it isn't meant to be a word."

"Well, what is it?" I asked.

"It isn't a word," he said emphasizing the "a," "it's a word square."

"You could have fooled me!" I replied.

"Are you complaining?" he demanded.

"Not at all, no, certainly not," I replied, beating a hasty retreat and twisting my brain to see a word square in PASTERNES. Then I realized where it was. Can you find it?

56. Altogether Now

Peter has been making tracks with the train set he was given for Christmas. This layout has four straight sections, W, X, Y and Z, each long enough to take the engine and three cars. At the moment the engine is on X and one car is on each of the other straight sections. What is the shortest distance the engine can travel in order to have all the cars in line in one of the straight sections with the engine ready to pull them out?

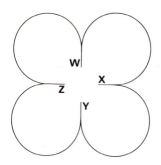

57. Four Shorties

DOUBLE YOUR MONEY

"Don't forget that you owe me five pence!" said Fred.

"What!" replied Tom, "Five pence isn't worth bothering about."

"All right then," said Fred, "you can give me ten pence."

What is the logic behind Fred's reply?

A REAL TWISTER

You have a cardboard cylinder, a length of cotton, ink and newspaper, and nothing else. How can you draw an accurate helix (a screw shape with uniform pitch) on the outside of the cylinder?

A COVER-UP JOB

By suitably placing a six-inch square over a triangle I can cover up to three-quarters of the triangle. By suitably placing the triangle over the square, I can cover up to one-half of the square. What is the area of the triangle?

AN ALTERNATIVE SOLUTION

"Is this sentence unusual in word order, seems not quite so correct M'lud." Can you make sense out of this, or these?

58. Four More Shorties

FIVE IN A ROW

A certain word, if carelessly written so that one of the letters is not quite completed, may become five consecutive letters of the alphabet. What is it? •

FOR PEDESTRIANS ONLY

When is it polite to overtake or pass on the inside only?

LETTERS PLAY

What letter in the alphabet comes after T, E, L, H, B?

A SIMPLE RULE

You are given a rectangular piece of paper, a pencil and a ruler with two parallel edges but no other markings of any kind. Construct an angle of 30°.

59. Figure It

What are the next three numbers, reading from top to bottom?

2	7	3	11	
5	1	9	1	
4	3	5	7	

60. Plane and Simple

This diagram shows a cube, in perspective, with what appears at first sight to be a plane slice taken off, removing two corners. All you have to do is to decide whether it *could* indeed be a plane slice—or whether appearances are deceptive.

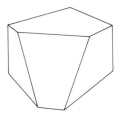

61. Locking Polyominoes

A polyomino is a shape made up from a number of unit squares joined complete edge to complete edge. Each of these two polyominoes is composed of 25 small squares and you will notice that these two pieces interlock, like pieces of a jigsaw puzzle, and also that they can be used to tile the complete plane, continuing forever in every direction.

However, they are not the smallest polyominoes which interlock in this manner, with the same property. What *is* the smallest polyomino which will tile the plane, such that each piece interlocks individually with each adjacent piece? And what is the smallest polyomino tile if the condition is only that the tessellation as a whole is interlocking, even if individual pieces are not?

62. To and Fro

Inspector Brobin had been on the trail of the same gang for months. Every time he thought that he had them cornered, they would take off into the night and he would arrive in time to clear up the mess they left behind. Sunday morning was no exception—a few burnt scraps in the grate, food half-eaten in the kitchen and empty bottles in the dustbin. The Inspector was just about to leave one of his minions in charge and go home to Sunday breakfast when he was handed a scrap of material that, though burnt, had not disintegrated. On it he could make out this sequence of letters and blank spaces.

Was it a code? Did it mean anything?

A I T N--T Y H A E D-N D U O S G--E A G N D D I-
R P T A R

63. Fours into Nine

This is the grid for a children's crossword, in which no word of more than four letters will be used. Apart from this restriction, the grid will obey the usual rule that the black squares do not separate any part of the puzzle completely from the remainder.

What is the smallest number of black squares that must be filled in in order to satisfy these conditions?

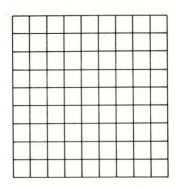

SOLUTIONS

1. Chris's Kisses

"Chris kissed Cross but Cross crossed Chris so Chris's kris criss-crossed Cross; now krised Cross's crossing kisses caress Chris no more."

A kris is a wavy-bladed Indonesian dagger. The word kris can also be used as a verb.

2. Missing Quickie

You would expect to see it on a shop door. It is a CLOSED/OPEN sign from which the grill, which alternately covers the letters of one of the words and then the other, is missing.

3. Bridgit's Bar

Two of the differences between three numbers will sum to the third difference, so you are looking for a number somewhat less than 250 which can be represented as the product of three factors, such that one factor is the sum of the other two (in more than one way, because you are told that the information is ambiguous).

The required number is 240, which can be represented as *three* different products with the necessary property:

$$240 = 16 \times 15 \times 1 = 12 \times 10 \times 2 = 10 \times 6 \times 4.$$

The puzzle does not say, obviously, that Bridgit's age can be deduced, whichever of these three possibilities is correct. It cannot possibly be deduced. It does say that Bridgit's age could be *reached*, whichever of the possibilities is chosen. Since double Graham's age plus David's age will be an expression of the form $3B \pm X$, and we shall find Bridgit's age, B, by equating this with $4B - 2$, we must look for arrangements of ages, one for each possibility, which will lead to the same expressions $3B \pm X$.

These arrangements of ages are:

2,10,12	$B - 2, B, B + 10$
1,15,16	$B, B + 1, B + 16$
4,6,10	$B, B + 4, B + 10,$

each of which can lead, with a suitable identification of Graham and David, to the expression $3B + 18$ for double Graham's age plus David's. No other arrangements of the ages will do.

Solving $3B + 18 = 4B - 2$, we discover that Bridgit is 20 years old.

4. Behind the Scenes

The original scores of 6 points to each finalist must have come from a first, second and third placing each. When the three dishonest singers reversed their order of marking, the 3 points and 1 point scored by the honest singer was reversed, but his total remained at 6. The other three finalists, however, when the marks were reversed, gained 2, lost 2, or stayed the same, depending on whether they scored 1, 2 or 3 from the honest singer. So the final scores were 8, 6, 6 and 4, and the honest man was tied second.

5. Sizzling Sermon

The curate's writing was rather cramped so that the gaps between the words were not obvious. Leaving the letters exactly as given, but putting the spaces in the correct position, and giving it the punctuation that the curate would have used in delivering it, the sermon began, "Unclean! Dishallowed! Evil!. . . ." —a vigorous start but not one which reflected in any way on his relative.

6. Giving Change

He started with two 50p coins, spent 30p, leaving 50p, 10p and 10p; next spent 3p, leaving 50p, 10p, 5p and 2p; then

then finally spent ½p (a very difficult feat), leaving 50p, 10p, 5p, 1p and ½p. Total expenditure: 33½p.

7. *Looking Both Ways*

The garage-like building is actually an electricity supply depot with concertina doors. The words on the door are on consecutive panels, which of course face alternately in two directions. The whole message is: ELECTRICITY SUPPLY DEPOT PLEASE KEEP CLEAR AT ALL TIMES and on the way back I see, in the same pattern as the puzzle figure, LCRCT UPY EO LAEKE CERA ALTMS.

8. *Groovy Sequences*

The defining characteristic of a GROOVY sequence can be described best by referring to the first example: 1 2 2 2 2 3 4 8 9. The last digit, 9, is the total number of numbers in the sequence. Eight is the total number, excluding all the 1s. Four is the number remaining when the 1s and 2s are omitted, and so on. Geometrically, such a pattern may be shown as a pattern of dots in a right angle, which is symmetrical about the bisector of the right angle, as our figure shows. Reading the number of dots in each row from the top downwards produces the first GROOVY sequence; and it is clear that the number of rows, nine, is equal to the number of dots in the last row, also nine, and so on. So the completed fourth sequence is: 1 1 2 2 4 6.

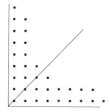

9. *Relative Volumes*

A regular tetrahedron, that is, a triangular pyramid all of whose edges are equal, can be dissected into four identical tetrahedrons and an octahedron, as in our figure. The edges of these pieces are all equal to each other and to one-half of the original edges of the large tetrahedron. The volumes of similar solids are in proportion to the cubes of the ratio of their edges. One-half cubed is one-eighth. So each small tetrahedron is one-eighth the volume of the original, and four of them are half that volume. The octahedron, which is two square pyramids face to face, is also one-half the original volume. So each square pyramid is double the volume of the triangular pyramid with equal edges.

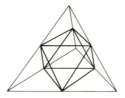

10. Parallelepiped

The squares cannot be the faces of the parallelepiped, so the squares' edges must be its edges, and the squares must be suitably taped to give the necessary rigidity. Here is how it is done:

The parallelepiped is the interior hole in the center of the model. The remarkable feature of this formation is its flexibility. It will in fact form a cube, but can also be squashed completely flat, without distortion, and in-between forms every possible parallelepiped with equal edges. Moreover, by adding four more square faces to each of the remaining faces of the parallelepiped (as shown by our dotted lines), the parallelepiped becomes completely enclosed but is still just as flexible. Even more surprisingly, if you imagine identical parallelepipeds fixed to each of the six open ends of the figure, and build rings of four squares round each of the remaining faces, and so on, you can construct a three-dimensional network which could be extended in theory to fill the whole of space. The network divides space into two identical interpenetrating parts, and it will still collapse into a plane or assume any position in between!

11. Tell Me the Way To Go Home

This is the only possible position for Tom Farley's home.

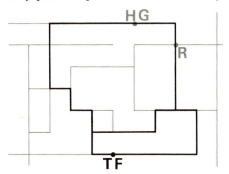

12. Parking Lot

A solution is possible only if two parts each contain *separate,* but matching, front and rear halves of one make.

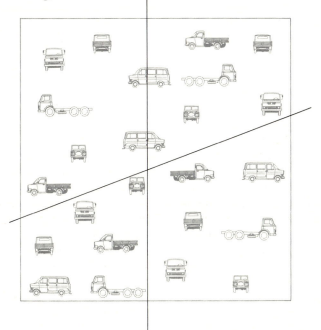

13. Triangular Trisection

This is the minimum solution, in only five pieces. One-third is the central kite. Pair each large triangle with one small triangle to get two more identical kites.

14. The Walrus and the Carpenter

"You are very shellfish!"

15. Unsymmetrical Symmetry

There are seven arrangements of ten men satisfying the given conditions. This is the only one of the seven which is not symmetrical:

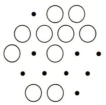

16. A Mon-ster Puzzle

Two pieces; in other words, neither square need be more than partially cut through. Both squares are cut along the length of a diagonal cross through the center, and in one only, one arm of the cross is continued into the corner. The two squares can now be interlaced to form the *mon*.

17. *To Separate or Not To Separate*

The cube can be made as two separable pieces. The easiest way to see this is to imagine that the cuts actually reach into the corners, instead of stopping three-quarters of an inch short from each edge. The cube would then be divided into six slices which would slide freely along the long diagonal. By making the cuts stop short of the corner, so joining three slices together, the single piece will slide out more freely than a single slice.

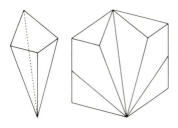

18. *April Fool*

The heavy lines show how the letters can be cut into seven pieces which form a large square with a smaller square attached. Cutting along the dotted lines now divides these two squares into pieces which will exactly fill the dotted square. (The last step is a simple example of techniques discussed in another Dover book, *Recreational Problems in Geometric Dissections and How To Solve Them* by Harry Lindgren.)

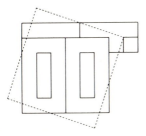

19. *Skew Addition*

The answer is simply the sequence of digits that repeats in the decimal fraction for ⅐: 142857142857142. . . . . One way to prove this is to think of the sum as simply $\frac{1}{10} + \frac{3}{100} + \frac{9}{1000}$ . . ., which sums to ⅐. Another is to start dividing 7 into 10, like this: 7 into

10 goes 1 time, remainder 3; 7 into 30 goes 3 times (because 30 is
3 ×10), with remainder 9; 7 into 90 goes 9 times, remainder 27;
and so on. The result is a decimal which equals ⅟₇, in which the
digits overlap just as in our sum.

20. *Addled Ladders*

At one moment in time the smallest gap between the ladders is
one-third of the distance between successive rungs (minus a bit
for the thickness of each rung). Any rearrangement of the three
sets of rungs will leave a gap larger than this somewhere.

Over a period of time as the rungs of two ladders momentarily
coincide, the gap between the overlapping rungs and the rungs of
the third ladder must be at least one-half of the distance between
the rungs. Mr. and Mrs. Newly would only fail to see such a gap
if the two ladders moving right were going at nearly the same
speed.

21. *To Spy or Not To Spy*

22. A Double Strip

The area of overlap is one-half of the area of a parallelogram whose height is the width of the strip and whose base is greater than or equal to the width of the strip. The overlap area will be a minimum when this parallelogram is a square and the strip is folded at right angles.

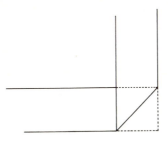

23. Electronic Lullaby

If the first two notes are *mmmmm–mmmmm*, then it will settle down and play *mmmmm* for ever. If the first two notes are anything else, then it soon settles into this rather over-simple tune: *ping–boing–ping–boing–ping–boing.* . . .

24. A Giant Difference

According to the conditions of the problem, all the differences which have to be added together are just the differences between the numbers to be placed in the five black squares, and the white squares adjacent to them. No differences between two white ·squares or two black squares are involved. So the maximum differences will be obtained by either placing the five smallest numbers in the black squares, or the five largest numbers there.

In addition, the central square makes four differences with the white squares, so this square should contain 9 if the white squares are low, and 1 otherwise.

Once these conditions are satisfied, the order in which the numbers are placed is irrelevant. Changing the order of the numbers will increase and decrease the differences by the same amount.

Here are two solutions, one of each type. The maximum difference is 58, which can be calculated as 3 (6 + 7 + 8 + 9) − 4 × 1 − 2 (2 + 3 + 4 + 5).

5	2	8
3	9	1
7	4	6

2	6	5
7	1	9
3	8	4

25. An Odd Problem

An even number of lines go to every circle except the two middle circles. However, if one of the lines going to a middle circle is taken away, that middle circle will then be even but the circle at the other end of the line which is removed will become odd. The process of taking a line away will then have to be repeated, again and again, until a line is taken away which ends on the other middle circle.

In other words, the smallest number of lines which can be removed is the number in the shortest route from one middle circle to the other. So three lines must be removed, and this can be done in either of two ways.

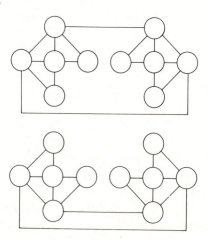

26. Maid To Tease

She must omit at least four rooms each day. The first diagram shows the rooms divided in a checkerboard pattern. The maid inevitably goes from a black room to a white room and then to a black room and so on. Since there are 15 white rooms and only 10 black, the most she can visit is 11 white and 10 black, starting and ending in a white room. Four rooms, all of the white type, must be omitted.

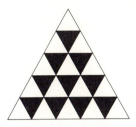

Here is one simple way of doing this, which can obviously be extended to any larger triangle, missing one extra room for each extra row of triangles added.

27. Table Cross

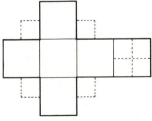

The right-hand square is quartered, and re-sewn as in this diagram. This non-square will cover a square table very well!

28. Double Riddle

The two associated solutions are CHRISTMAS and BOXING DAY. (In England, Boxing Day is the day following Christmas, when tradesmen traditionally visited their customers and received a "box" or present.)

29. Brass or Rubber

The solution depends on the fact that if there are three rings which interlock in the manner represented by the diagram, then one of the rings must be flexible if they are all to lie flat. Note that, moving in a clockwise direction, each ring goes over each successive ring. Three rings with this property are called Borromean rings, after the Italian family which used them as their heraldic emblem.

In this puzzle, C is over D which is over E which is over C, so one of these rings must be flexible. Similarly, one of D, B and C is rubber and so is one of A, B and C. The only common ring is C, which is therefore the flexible ring.

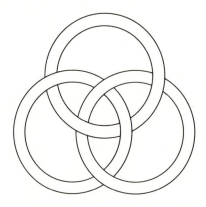

30. Start Counting

There are 64 triangles in all. This remarkably high total is most easily calculated, (or the general formula calculated), by temporarily removing the base of the triangle, as in our figure.

Every triangle in this reduced figure has a vertex at either *A* or *B* and all the triangles can be picked out by choosing, say, two lines through *A* and then choosing one line through *B* for the base of the triangle. This must be repeated with pairs of line through *B* and lines through *A* as bases.

There are 6 ways to choose a pair of lines through *A* and 4 possible bases through *B*. Total, 24 triangles. Repeated with pairs of lines through *B*, this adds another 24 triangles. Now return the base of the original triangle. Any line through *A* (4 choices), plus any line through *B* (4 choices), will make a triangle with the original base. Grand total: $4 \times 4 + 24 + 24 = 64$ triangles.

The general formula for a triangle, two of whose sides are divided into *n* parts each, is $2 \times n(\frac{1}{2}n^2 - \frac{1}{2}n) + n^2 = n^3$. A satisfyingly simple result!

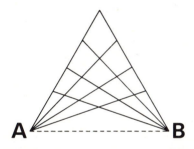

31. Can-Can Strip

The answer is $4\frac{1}{2}$ inches, one-half of the circumference of the can. The height of the can and the width of the strip are totally irrelevant. If the strip covers one-half of the can's curved surface, then it will cover one-half of the surface of any slice of the can parallel to its ends, including in the limit the circumference of the can itself.

32. Rice Division

This is the shape her husband produced. The size and proportions of the base are irrelevant as long as the base and sides of the box are rectangles. It will be possible to choose the height of the cut at each corner, and then make the cut with just one stroke of the sword, so that by measuring from the appropriate corner, either one, two, three or four measures can be measured. The technique is to fill the box so that the rice has a level surface, just comes up to the lip of the chosen corner, and leaves the opposite corner of the base rectangle just showing.

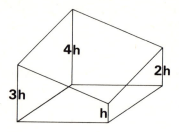

33. U or Non-U?

Of these two solutions, the first generalizes to rectangles of any size, in a very simple manner.

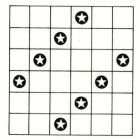 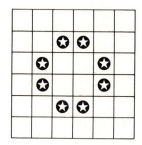

34. World Without End

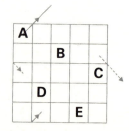

This arrangement is one solution. The five points are in a straight line in the order ABCDE and also in a straight line at right-angles to the first in the order ADBEC. However, this last line must be drawn by going from A to D off the top edge and continuing to travel roughly NNE. Traveling roughly SSE from A to D gives a line ADBEC which is at right-angles to the line AEDCB when that line is drawn in a direction roughly ENE.

35. Trigger Happy

The phrase, "it reads the same either way" did *not* mean that it was palindromic. It meant that it read the same upside down as the right way up! It was in fact 263^2 which is 69169. This was the code number.

36. The Language of Animals

All these creatures may be found, in this order (no penalty for missing the last one—it depends on what is meant by "hidden"): bear, rat, wasp, asp, rabbit, ape, eel, dingo, snake, cow, ant, hare, hen, owl, carp, bee, tench, gar, heron, eland, sole.

37. Dudley No More

The two sums are: $13 + 93 = 106$, and $106 + 136 = 242$.

$P = 1$, since the sum of two two-digit numbers cannot exceed 198. Therefore D must be at most 3; since it is even, $D = 2$. So T must be 1 or 6, and so $T = 6$. Similarly, A is 8 or 3 in order to give $T = 6$ in the first sum. But if $A = 8$, then $M = 9$ and $E = 1$, which is impossible. So $A = 3$, $M = 9$ and $E = 0$, from the first sum. Completing the second sum, $U = 4$.

38. A Boiling Problem

The students' system will generally be fair. If it is not, then they are using the fire in *too regular* a pattern. For example, they might use between them exactly five pence worth of electricity per day, each using the fire at the same time of day for the same length of time each day. In this case, one student would always be the one to put in the fivepenny piece.

They should be advised to make their use of the fire *less regular,* or of course to change to another method of dividing the cost.

39. The Chipped Bowl

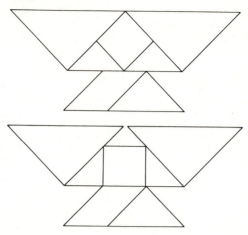

40. A Bed of Roses

Nine square yards. A Mr. G. Pick is credited with discovering in 1899 that the area of any shape formed by joining intersections of a square grid with straight lines is one less than the number of intersections inside the boundary, plus half the number of intersections on the boundary. In this case there are 7 corner points inside, and the only points on the boundary are the 6 boundary stakes.

$$7 - 1 + \tfrac{1}{2}(6) = 9$$

If the reader is not familiar with this theorem (!) a little experimentation with possible shapes will soon convince him that all shapes with the given properties have the same area of 9 units—even if the reader does not feel like proving Pick's theorem by representing every shape as a set of rectangles with some right-angled triangles removed. Here are two examples of shapes that fit the puzzle:

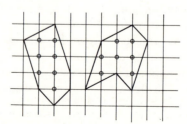

41. Not Quite Useless

The machine which will only subtract is most useful as it can substitute for all the others. To add 79 and 52 for example, work out successively: 500 − 79, (500 − 79) − 52, and 500 − (500 − 79 − 52), where the number 500 can be replaced by any other large number. Multiplication and division can be replaced by repeated additions and subtractions.

The adding machine can only stand in for subtraction by using addition from the lower number which is not totally automatic, as an appreciation of the nearness of the total to the higher number is required. For example, to subtract 256 from 810 would require something like: adding 400, then another 100, then 50, then 4, and then totaling the numbers added to 554. Clearly this cannot be described as automatic, since the person operating the machine has to see when the total is approaching 810.

42. An Intimate Affair

Four men and four women were present. If you mark points for individual men and women, joining dancing partners by lines, then you will construct a skeleton of points and lines in which, according to the information given, every area has four edges and three edges meet at every point. All skeletons with these properties are equivalent either to a single cube or to several entirely separate cubes. Since the soirée is described as intimate, it is reasonable to suppose that the skeleton is one cube only, as in our diagram. There is one person for each of the eight vertices of the cube.

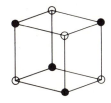

43. A Cushy Number

He can check the direction of his shots easily, because a shot parallel to a cush will return through its starting point after six rebounds. (We did say that the cushions were perfect!) At whatever point he starts, the total distance traveled before return is equal to the total perimeter of the triangle. So by conveniently timing his shots, the Professor could check their strength as well.

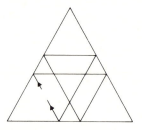

44. The Golden Handshake

The number of pieces received by each member must be a common factor of 20 and 10. One or 2 would imply that 30 or 15 men arrived late, which cannot be described as a handful. Ten pieces each implies that the last members to arrive were one man, which is impossible. So each man received 5 gold pieces and 6 men arrived late. The number of men originally present was little more than 30, because all but a handful could have received an extra gold piece. Also, the total number of members is divisible by 6. So 36 men were present originally, and 42 men are gang members.

45. Artful Arithmetic

Johnny's method is perfectly valid and very quick. If $\frac{2}{5}$ is smaller than $\frac{3}{7}$, then $\frac{2}{5}$ will be smaller in proportion to $(1-\frac{2}{5})$ than $\frac{3}{7}$ will be to $(1-\frac{3}{7})$. In other words, $\frac{2}{5}:\frac{3}{5}$ will be less than $\frac{3}{7}:\frac{4}{7}$, and so $\frac{2}{3}$ will be less than $\frac{3}{4}$. This argument can be repeated as many times as necessary.

46. A Non-Slippery Problem

The diameter of A is $\frac{2}{3}$ the diameter of D, so the speed of D will be $\frac{2}{3}$ the speed of A. The sizes and speeds of rotation of B and C are irrelevant to the solution. To see this, imagine a point on the circumference of A as it passes the point of contact with B. Any point on the circumference of B will travel at the same *linear* speed, because the rollers are not slipping against each other; the circumference of *D* will travel at the same linear speed also.

47. Coming and Going

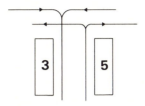

48. Word Squares Made Easy

These are the two possible solutions. Two months after this puzzle was published, Darryl Francis in his "Wordrow" column in *Games & Puzzles* produced several other four-by-four word squares with only two letters, and then pointed out, amazingly, that since TOOTTOOT and OTTOOTTO are both words, they can be combined to make an eight-by-eight word square using only two letters. TOOT-TOOT is found as an exclamation in the *English Dialect Dictionary*, and OTTO-OTTO is an eight-eight time in music!

T	O	O	T
O	T	T	O
O	T	T	O
T	O	O	T

O	T	T	O
T	O	O	T
T	O	O	T
O	T	T	O

49. Advanced Word Maths

R	A	P	T
A	L	E	E
P	E	A	N
T	E	N	D

ALEE means on or towards the lee-side. A PEAN is a variety of heraldic fur, as well as being a variant spelling, both of PAEN (a song of triumph or thanksgiving) and of PEEN (the end of the hammerhead opposite the face).

50. Speedy Gonzales

I had dashed onto the platform at the rear end of the first train; I knew that the exit at my destination station was at the front end of the train, so I walked down the platform and reached the other end just as the next train arrived and I got into the front carriage. Result: I had quite simply walked the length of the train at the first station, instead of at my destination station, and no time was wasted at all.

51. Youth and Age

Grandfather's age must be an even square, and the difference between Grandfather's ages, when Patsy reaches half his present age and when Patsy was born, is one-half of his present age. Since the differences between successive squares are the odd numbers in sequence, one-half of Grandfather's present age must be representable as the sum of an even number of consecutive odd numbers which are the differences between his present age and the squares immediately above and below it.

A quick check shows that $\frac{1}{2} \times 64 = 32 = 15 + 17$ fits, making Patsy 15 and Grandfather 64. Checking successive higher even squares, they are further and further from fitting this pattern, so this is the unique solution.

52. Round the Bends

The bookshelves are 10 feet long, double the length of the piano. Since the corridor is of equal width on both sides, it is intuitively obvious (which means that we shall not prove it here!) that the tightest squeeze in getting the piano and the shelves round the corner will be when they are placed symmetrically with respect to the corner, as in this figure. The maximum length of the bookshelves will be the base of this triangle, and the piano is represented by the largest rectangle which will fit into the triangle, base on base.

Using the notation of the figure, the area of the rectangle and the remaining area are respectively,

$$2bx\,(a - x) \text{ and } bx^2 + bx\,(a - x) \times \frac{(a - x)}{x}.$$

A little elementary algebra reveals that the difference between these quantities is $b(a - 2x)^2$ which is a minimum, zero, when $x = \frac{1}{2}a$. Thus the area of the rectangle is a maximum when it is one-half the area of the triangle, and its base, in particular, is one-half the base of the triangle. So the shelves are $2 \times 5 = 10$ feet long (or a very little under 10 feet if you want to take into account the thickness of the wood of the bookshelves).

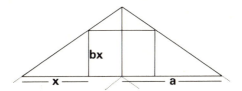

53. Beet This

The simplest shape consists of two infinite parallel planes, each divided into a checkerboard pattern, with every other square of one color, as it were, omitted and the edges of the omitted squares joined by four squares to the corresponding edges of the omitted square in the other plane. Other shapes with the same property can be derived from this by using an infinite number of planes.

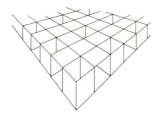

54. An Amazing Escape

This is the shortest route. Most attempts to get through the maze end up with Theseus unable to leave without omitting his last chance to turn right or left. His wander round the lower right corner is necessary to change the parity with which he approaches the north exit.

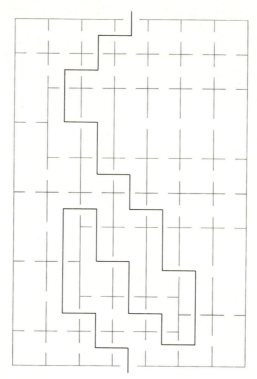

55. *Pasternes*

The word square is formed as in this diagram. This square has the neat feature that each minor diagonal, from lower left to top right, consists of one letter repeated. It is only because of this property that it can be summarized in the one word PASTERNES.

TERNE means sheet iron coated with an alloy of lead and zinc. An ERNE is an eagle.

P	A	S	T	E
A	S	T	E	R
S	T	E	R	N
T	E	R	N	E
E	R	N	E	S

56. Altogether Now

Twice the distance round the track. One solution is: the engine from X picks up the car at Y, continues to Z and picks up a second car. It leaves Z pushing the Y car and pulling the Z car, and continues to W. It leaves W towards X pushing the Z car and pulling the Y and W cars which it leaves on the curved track somewhere between W and X. The engine with Z continues in the same direction round the track for a second time finally pushing all three cars into X.

57. Four Shorties

DOUBLE YOUR MONEY

Tom thinks that Fred should not mind being five pence short, so presumably he will not mind himself being five pence short, which is what he would be if he gave Fred ten pence—which will naturally also satisfy Fred.

A REAL TWISTER

Inking the cotton and trying to wrap it evenly round the cylinder will never produce an accurate result. Instead, lay the newspaper on the flat floor, ink the cotton and stretch it in a straight line across the paper. Then simply roll the cylinder across the cotton at an angle. By varying the angle at which the cylinder crosses the cotton you can vary the pitch of the helix.

A COVER-UP JOB

When the square covers as much of the triangle as possible, the triangle will automatically overlap the square as much as possible. So three-quarters of the triangle equals one-half of the square, which is 18 square inches, and the area of the triangle is 24 square inches.

AN ALTERNATIVE SOLUTION

Taking alternate words, we get two separate sentences: "Is sentence in order, not so M'lud," and, "This unusual word seems quite correct."

58. Four More Shorties

FIVE IN A ROW

ABODE becomes ABCDE if the O is not quite completed.

FOR PEDESTRIANS ONLY

When walking up or down a spiral staircase. The insides of the steps are narrower than the outsides and more difficult to walk on.

LETTERS PLAY

T: the given letters are alternate letters in the two words, THE ALPHABET.

A SIMPLE RULE

Draw three parallel lines with one ruler-width separating each of them. Then place the ruler as in the diagram. Imagining the perpendicular from the corner to the edge of the ruler, the triangle ABC is one-half of an equilateral triangle, and the angle at A is 30°.

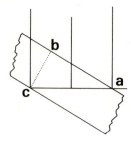

59. Figure It

Reading from top to bottom, the numbers are 3, 17, 5. Three is the difference between 11 and 1 + 7. Seventeen is the difference between 1 and 11 + 7, and 5 is the difference between 7 and 11 + 1.

60. Plane and Simple

If the slice is a plane one, then since the top and bottom faces of the original cube are parallel, the two lines *ac* and *bd* will be parallel. However, to discover whether two lines are parallel in a perspective drawing is not trivial, so a little more cunning is required.

Reconstruct the missing edge, *E.* Then *ab* will meet *E*, because both lines lie in one face of the cube. Similarly, *cd* meets *E.* IF *abcd* is a plane slice, then *ab* and *cd* will meet. In this case all three lines must meet in the same point, because all three lines do not lie in the same plane.

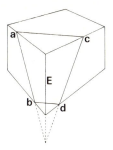

Checking in the solution diagram, they do indeed *appear* to meet in the same point and so the slice *could* be a plane one. If it is not, it is only because its surface is not plane although its edges lie in one plane.

61. Locking Polyominoes

In all honesty I felt that I had to include in this collection a puzzle which at the time of composing I got completely wrong. This is it. Originally, the puzzle diagram was my "answer" (I had assumed with no good reason that pieces would interlock individually), but many readers of *Games & Puzzles* wrote in to point out that at the very least I should have considered the possibility that the overall pattern interlocked without individual pieces interlocking, and that with this milder constraint there were many smaller solutions.

Bob Newman sent in the most complete set of examples, from which the following are selected. Diagram 1 shows individually-interlocking 21-ominoes. Diagram 2 shows pieces interlocking over the whole plane, which are doubly symmetric and only 18-ominoes. The 14-ominoes in diagram 3 happen to have point symmetry, but the occurrence of symmetry in these examples may be quite irrelevant to the problem—diagram 1 could scarcely be less symmetrical. Finally, if half the pieces are allowed to be turned over, then the 12-ominoes in diagram 4 will do the trick.

There is some reason to suppose that diagrams 2 & 3 are minimal solutions, but I have no proof that this is so and all four diagrams may be improvable.

62. *To and Fro*

The material was a length of typewriter ribbon, the last few inches before the spool, and the letters were spaced so that the message in a forward direction alternated, letter by letter, with the continuation of the same message after the spool had automatically changed direction. So we read out this suggestive fragment: AT THE DOG AND PARTRIDGE SUNDAY NI.

63. *Fours into Nine*

Clearly every row and every column must contain at least one black square, and naive solutions using eighteen black squares are numerous. Solutions with seventeen black squares are not difficult to find, starting with our first diagram, based on the ubiquitous knight's move. For sufficiently large initial squares this no doubt provides the absolute minimum, since the distances between black squares, either horizontally or vertically, are exactly four squares.

However, thanks to the small size of the initial square, a smaller solution with only sixteen blacked-out squares is possible. Our second diagram shows one such solution. The author is convinced that this *is* a minimum—but cannot prove it mathematically.

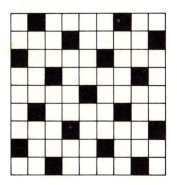 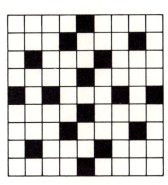